THE WHISKY CONNOISSEUR'S BOOK OF DAYS

Facts, Fables and Folklore

John Lamond

THE WHISKY CONNOISSEUR'S BOOK OF DAYS

John Lamond

First published in the United Kingdom by The Edinburgh Publishing Company Limited, Whittingehame, East Lothian, Scotland.

British Library Cataloguing in Data
Lamond, John
Whisky Connoisseur's Book of Days, 1993
I. Title
641.2
ISBN 1 872401 02 1

Cover illustration: Highland Hospitality by John Frederick Lewis (1805-76) by kind permission of the Fine Art Society, Edinburgh and The Bridgeman Art Library, London.

Printed and bound in the United Kingdom by
Stephens & George Ltd, Merthyr Industrial Estate, Dowlais, Merthyr Tydfil, Mid Glamorgan, CF48 2TD

CONTENTS

Just as, over the centuries Scotland has set the standard for whisky, so, since 1783, Waterford Crystal has set the standard for hand made and hand cut glass.

In that year two brothers, George and William Penrose began manufacturing crystal glass in the city of Waterford in Ireland, and soon their products were welcomed with growing enthusiasm in the aristocratic houses of Europe and America.

They dedicated themselves to producing crystal with a purity of colour and a depth and intricacy of cut that remains the hallmark of the glass produced by Waterford Crystal today.

Thus, the brilliance of the crystal, its reassuring weight, and vivacious sparkle all combine to transform the drinking of the world's finest whiskies from a simple enjoyment into a memorable experience.

WATERFORD® CRYSTAL

For further information please contact:

Waterford Wedgwood plc

Barlaston

Stoke-on-Trent

ST12 9ES

Tel: 0782 204141

Waterford ® Crystal is a registered trademark of Waterford Wedgwood plc, Kilbarry, Waterford, Ireland.

INTRODUCTION

The myths and legends regarding that most wondrous of drinks are legion. It is said to lengthen life; ease pain and sickness; promote friendship; banish quarrels and even to cross language barriers. There are whiskies for every mood, time, season, place and occasion. It is the basis of many cocktails, and one or two liqueurs, and an excellent aperitif and digestif. It has been used for centuries as a drink for celebration, for mourning, as a medicine, and just for sheer enjoyment.

To fully savour the complexities of this most unique of drinks, one should not merely drink it. To allow the beauties of the flavour to fully develop, I recommend adding one part water to two parts whisky - the size of the measure I leave entirely up to you! Gently swill the glorious liquid around in your glass; gaze at the golden colour and deeply inhale the exquisite bouquet. Savour this fully; identify as many aroma characters as you can, and only then raise the glass to your lips. I promise that you will taste whisky as you have never tasted it before.

This book is designed to be used both as a day book and as a source of information and pleasure. Use it to keep a note of all your important engagements, as an aide memoire, and enjoy the stories as you would your whiskies. Dip into them as often, and for as long, as you wish. Fill those long winter evenings in front of the fire with a dram of your favourite cratur and this book to while away the hours, or perhaps lower the temperature of those heady days of summer with an ice cube or two in your water of life. However you choose to use the book, enjoy it!

Slainte!

John Lamond
Larkhall, Lanarkshire, Scotland

THE CORRECT GAELIC PRONUNCIATION

The correct pronunciation of distillery names has long been a source of embarrassment for those interested in the subject. Scots Gaelic (pronounced *gal-ik*, while the Irish is pronounced *gay-lik*), is not exactly the easiest language to pronounce from the written word. Below are listed some of the most frequently encountered distillery and Gaelic names, with their phonetic spellings in italics:

Aberlour	*Aber-lower*
Allt-a' Bhainne	*Olt-a-bane*
Auchroisk	*Othrusk*
Auchentoshan	*Ochentoshan*
Balmenach	*Bal-MAY-nach*
Bruichladdich	*Brew-ich-laaddie*
Bunnahabhain	*Boon-a-havun*
Caol Ila	*Kaal-eela*
Cardhu	*Kar-doo*
Clynelish	*Klyne-leesh*
Craigellachie	*Krai-GELLachy*
Dailuaine	*Dall-YEWan*
Dallas Dhu	*Dallas Doo*
Edradour	*Edra-dower*
Gaugers	*Gay-jers*
Glen Garioch	*Glen GEE-ree*
Glenglassaugh	*Glen Glass-och*
Glen Mhor	*Glen Voar*
Glenmorangie	*Glen-MORanjee*
Glenury-Royal	*Glen-you-ree*
Glentauchers	*Glen-tockers*
Islay	*Eye-la*
Knockdhu	*Nock-doo*
Laphroaig	*La-froyg*
Old Pulteney	*Pult-nay*
Pittyvaich	*Pit-ee-vay-ich*
St. Magdalene	*Magdaleen*
Slainte Mhath	*Schlan-jer var*
Strathisla	*Strath-eye-la*
Tamdhu	*Tam-doo*
Tamnavulin	*Tamna-VOO-lin*
Teaninich	*Tee-an-inich*
Tomintoul	*Tomin-towel*
Tullibardine	*Tully Bard-eye-n*
Uisgebeatha	*Oos-gi-BAY-ha*

So exquisite is their cunning in gratifying their appetites that they have thus invented a method to make their water itself intoxicate.

        -Pliny (speaking of the Celts)

28

29

30

31

1

Ne'er Day

2

Went shooting I shot 1 partridge + 2 Phesants

1898-A 9 year old boy died from severe burns sustained after falling into a washback at Cragganmore where he was visiting with his uncle.

3

Broken + open, window at Benromach

1925-The Glenlivet celebrated their centenary.

ETHEREAL FLAVOUR

Christie's arranged for an invited audience to hear Richard Paterson, Master Blender at Whyte & Mackay, conduct a very special tutored tasting demonstrating the maturation stages of various whiskies. There were 10 samples of *Dalmore* from new spirit to 52 years old; 7 samples of *Fettercairn* from new spirit to 32 years old and some very interesting old grain whiskies: *Dumbarton* at 33 years old and *Lomond* at 30 years old. The 52 years old *Dalmore* was described as "an explosion on the palate and then, when it is swallowed, it goes down VERY smoothly - only for the ethereal flavour to rise again and last for hours."

WHISKY RARITIES

Christie's, the auctioneers, have for the past few years held an annual auction in Scotland at which rare and old bottles, as well as the odd miniature and item of whisky memorabilia, have come under the hammer. Each year the record sum paid for a bottle of scotch is raised further. At present this honour is held by the manager of a bar in Osaka, Japan who, in 1991, paid £6,375 for a 75cl bottle of *Macallan* which was distilled in 1926 and bottled in 1986; 60 years old or £212.50 for a single measure! Apparently one public house in Yorkshire picked up a bottle of 50 years old *Macallan* and sold the measures (1/6th of a gill) for £100 each. The bottle only lasted two months! Other oddities which have come under the hammer at *Christie's* have included a bottle of *White Horse*, bottled in 1940 which fetched £340.00, while a similar bottle, but bottled in 1951 only raised £200.00.

If a body could just find oot the exac' proper proportion and quantity that ought to be drunk every day, and keep to that, I verily trow that he might leev for ever, without dyin' at a', and that doctors and kirkyairds wid go oot o' fashion.

- James Hogg, *The Ettrick Shepherd*

Alas, poor Caledonia's mountaineer,
Whom want's stern edict e'er and feudal grief
had forced him from a home he loved so dear.
Yet found he here a home and glad relief
And plied the beverage from his own fair sheaf
That fired his Highland blood with mickle glee.
-Campbell, from Gertrude of Wyoming

An old Scotsman met a Yankee friend in New York and invited him for a dram.

"Weel," says Sandy, "what are ye for?"

"Oh, I guess I'll have Champagne," replies the New Yorker.

"Na, na," says Sandy, "ye'll need to guess again my man, ye'll need to guess again."

Inspiring, bold John Barleycorn!
What dangers thou canst make us scorn!
Wi' tippeny we fear nae evil;
Wi' uisgebae, we'll face the Devil!
— Robert Burns

4 Tidied up my room

1655-Robert Haig reprimanded by church elders for distilling on the Sabbath.

5 Aberdeen

1801-Chivas Brothers Ltd founded in Aberdeen.

6

1864-Tommy Dewar was born.

7

8

9 Strong winds

1840-Glen Albyn begins production.

10 Stormy ~~wild~~ winds + a bit of snow

1892-Collapse of roof at Glenspey distillery under 2 feet of snow.

WHYTE & MACKAY, MIDLAND STREET BOTTLING HALL, 1897

THE RISE OF BLENDED WHISKIES

The greatest catalyst to the worldwide success of Scotch Whisky was, strangely enough, the thing which destroyed the wine world from the 1860s, an aphid known as *Phylloxera Vastatrix*. This aphid came originally from the United States of America and attacked the vine's natural immune system. The vineyards were then destroyed by mildew, rot or some other disease of the vine. Because the vines were destroyed, no wine could be made. The gentry around the world drank brandy and soda and therefore something had to step into this gaping hole and take brandy's place. The art of blending malt and grain whiskies together had been perfected in the 1850s, so the end of the 19th century saw the rise of the "whisky barons", people like Tommy Dewar, John Buchanan and Lord Mackie and the worldwide market being created for Scotch Whisky.

THE QUALITY OF WHISKY ACCORDING TO AENEAS MACDONALD

Whisky - even inferior whisky - has a potency and a directness in the encounter which proclaims its sublime rank. It does not linger to toy with the senses, it does not seep through the body to the brain; it communicates through no intermediary with the core of a man, with the roots of his consciousness; it speaks from deep to deep. This quality of spiritual insistency derives from the physical nature of the liquid. Whisky is a re-incarnation; it is made by a sublimation of coarse and heavy barley malt; the spirit leaves the earthly body, disappears, and by a lovely metapsychosis returns in the form of a liquid exquisitely pure and impersonal. And thence whisky acquires that lightness and power which is so dangerous to the unwary, and so delightful to those who use it with reverence and propriety.

The grain is drowned in water by which its spirits are excited and set at liberty.

-Orosius and Isidorus (ancient Celtic chroniclers)

JANUARY

11 5"-6" of snow + wind.
Went to aberbor to get kilt fitted.
we might not be able to get back to school (what a shame)

12 Back to school

13

14

15 Finally returned to school

1920-Prohibition imposed on the citizens of the U.S.A.

16

17

There are two faces to whisky - *Malt Whisky* and *Grain Whisky*. Malt whisky is made from malted barley only. Malted barley is produced by soaking the grain in warm water and encouraging germination. During germination, the barley secretes the enzyme *diastase*, which makes the starch soluble. The unmalted cereals used in grain whisky production are cooked under pressure for about three and a half hours in *converters*, where starch cells in the grain, burst. This is added to the malted barley in the mash tun and the diastase in the malted barley converts the starch in the unmalted cereals, into sugar.

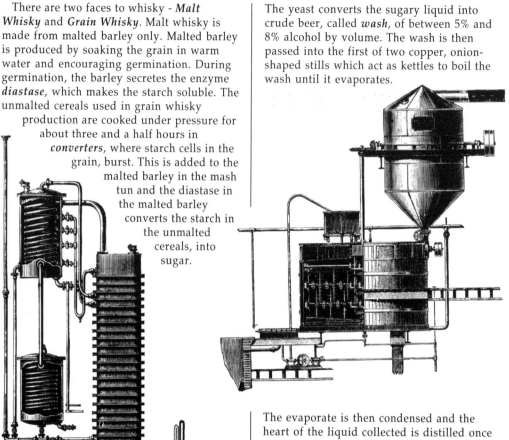

The yeast converts the sugary liquid into crude beer, called *wash*, of between 5% and 8% alcohol by volume. The wash is then passed into the first of two copper, onion-shaped stills which act as kettles to boil the wash until it evaporates.

The evaporate is then condensed and the heart of the liquid collected is distilled once again in the second still. The heart of this will, after three years maturation, become malt Scotch Whisky. Grain whisky other than malted barley also uses unmalted barley and other cereals.

At this stage, germination is stopped by blowing hot air, which is often (but not always) heated by burning peat, upwards through the malt. This adds flavour to the grain. The dried malt is ground in a mill and the *grist*, as it is now known, is mixed with heated water in a large circular vat called a *mash tun*. Here the soluble starch is drawn off from the mash tun and the solids, known as *draff*, are used for cattle fodder. Once cooled, the wort is filled into fermentation vessels known as *washbacks*, where yeast is added to it.

The character of Whisky is determined not by the purity of the spirit manufactured, but by the impurities left in the spirit.

-Major Douglas Mackessack of Glen Grant

18

1896-Glenburgie distillery sought estimates for the erection of the Customs Officer's house at the distillery.

19

1899-Pattisons Ltd., go into liquidation.

20

1835-Royal Warrant granted to Royal Brackla distillery by King William IV, who "has placed this first on the List of British Spirits."

21

22

23

24

1893-Mr. P. Mackenzie of Blair Athol distillery feued a site in Dufftown from Provost Symon for the erection of a distillery.

THE COFFEY STILL

Grain whisky is the product of a distillation in a continuous, patent or *Coffey Still*, where the wash goes into one end and, spirit ready for ageing, comes out of the other. The Coffey Still consists of two columns up to 60 feet high and called respectively an *analyser* and a *rectifier*. Steam is fed into the base of the analyser and hot wash into the top. The analyser is a series of horizontal, perforated plates. Where the steam and hot wash meet, the wash boils and a mixture of alcohol vapours and uncondensed steam rises to the top. Spent wash runs down and is led off the base. The hot vapours from the top of the analyser enter the base of the rectifier and, as they rise through the chambers, they partially condense on the sections of a long coil through which cold wash is flowing. The spirit vapour condenses at the top of the rectifier and is run off through a water-cooled condenser to the spirit safe. Once the spirit begins to run off, it runs continuously until the end of the distillation. Because of the rectifying element in the process, the distillate is generally lighter in aroma than most malt whiskies. It consequently has a milder character and requires less time to mature. A grain distillery is a much larger operation than a malt distillery.

A MUCH FELT WANT

In 1905, the Islington (London) Borough Council prosecuted two wine and spirit merchants for retailing whisky "not of the nature, substance and quality demanded". This developed into a battle between the predominantly Highland malt distillers and the predominantly Lowland grain distillers, led by The Distillers Company Ltd. A common blend consisted of 90% grain and 10% malt whiskies. In his judgement, which went against the patent distillers, the magistrate said, "I must hold that by Irish or Scotch Whisky is now meant a spirit obtained in the same methods by the aid of the form of still known as the pot still." D.C.L. marketed Cambus Single Grain with the slogan "not a headache in a gallon". A Royal Commission was set up in 1908 and William Ross of D.C.L., maintained in his testimony to the Commission: "Scotch Grain Whisky is supplying a much felt want for a lighter form of stimulant than is available in the heavy malt whiskies; it has increased the sale of these malt whiskies by the skilful manner in which it is blended therewith." The end result was the beginning of the legal definition of whisky.

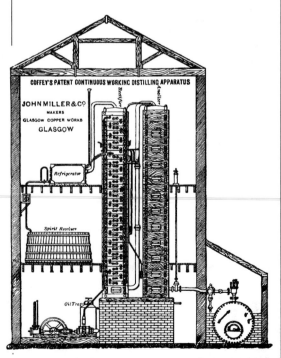

COFFEY'S PATENT CONTINUOUS WORKING DISTILLING APPARATUS

JOHN MILLER & Cº
MAKERS
GLASGOW COPPER WORKS
GLASGOW

From Greenwich Village to Left Bank cafes; from sushi bars in Downtown Tokyo to golfing hotels in the Scottish Highlands, it (Scotch Whisky) is at home.

-The Scotch Whisky Association

JANUARY

25

1759-Birthdate of Robert Burns.

26

1906-"What is Whisky?" case.

27

1958-Highland Distillers tell Banffshire Public Health Committee of their intention to open Glenglassaugh distillery which had not distilled since during World.War 1. They would need about 10,000 gallons of water per day.

28

1898-Glendullan receives its first consignment of barley

29

30

Wade House Over n right

1974-production starts at rebuilt Caol Ila distillery.
1644-Scots Parliament levies the first ever Excise Duty on Whisky.

31

⇒ WHON

1898-Speyburn distillery completed.

BELL'S®

THE PERFECT BLEND

The Bell's blend, with its nutty aroma and full spicy flavour has for years been unsurpassed in product quality. But, not willing to rest on past achievements, we are committed to strive for perfection in the blending of our whisky. There is no element of the process that escapes our attention.

GRAINS AND MALTS

The wide variety of over 35 different grain and malt whiskies that go into Bell's Extra Special are allowed to age a great deal longer than many of its competitors. To achieve that characteristic Bell's flavour and rich smooth aroma, the Bell's blend contains a particularly high malt content.

MATURED IN SHERRY CASKS

Producing the natural, attractive golden colour is also a finely judged craft. We do it by maturing a number of our malts in freshly emptied sherry casks.

UNIQUE BELL'S BLENDING

The meticulous blending process, which is continually enhanced and improved, ensures that every single bottle of Bell's attains the highest standards of quality associated with the finest old Scotch Whisky from Arthur Bell & Sons.

It could be argued that such a painstaking attitude is unnecessary in this day and age. We believe, though, that the end result more than justifies the effort.

THE PERFECT ENDING

AN AMELLIORATOR

Excessive drinking has long been a cause for concern with the clergy and Scotland has had its fair share of both. The climate and living conditions were harsh and anything which could soften the edges of life was firmly grasped with both hands! Whisky was such an amelliorator and thus the clergy faced an uphill task. The Rev. Mr. David Dunoon, minister of the parish of Killearnan in Ross-shire in the Statistical Account of 1796 said: "It will be asked, why then so many distilleries? For these reasons: distilling is almost the only method of converting our victual into cash for the payment of rent and servants; and whisky may, in fact be called our staple commodity. The distillers do not lay the proper value on their time and trouble, and of course look on all, but the price of the barley and the fine added to the tax, as clear profit; add to these the luxury of tasting the quality of the manufacture during the process."

THREE PINTS AND A MUTCHKIN

Whisky drinking was not always the civilised, peaceful, relaxing activity which we know today. An entry is recorded in *The Court Books of the Regality of Banff* in 1702 that three women were each ordered to be flogged thirty times for supplying spirit to "old Duncan Dow Donalich" and "young John Break" whilst these two were imprisoned at Castle Grant awaiting execution for robbery and murder. The record states that: **"Three pints and a mutchkin were conveyed to the prison by them and given to the said persons, and they drank till Donalich dyed thereby immediately, and young Break dyed throw the stress thereof going to the gallows."**

IMMODERATE DRINKING

Burt's *Letters from the North of Scotland* record that *"Some of the Highland Gentlemen are immoderate Drinkers of Usky - even three or four quarts at a sitting... Not long ago, four English Officers took a Foray to try their Strength in this Bow of Ulysses, against the like Number of the Country Champions, but the enemy came off victorious; and one of the Officers was thrown into a Fit of the Gout, without Hopes; another had a most dangerous Fever, a third lost his Skin and Hair by the Surfeit; and the last confessed to me, that when Drunkenness and Debate ran high he took several Opportunities to sham it."*

ARDENT SPIRITS

The Elgin Courant records on October 27th 1848 the "death of a boy from drinking ardent spirits." It appears that a 7 year old boy was left in charge of a spirit dealer's warehouse, while the proprietor, the boy's mother's landlord, went for breakfast. When he returned, he found the boy "insensible or sleeping from the effects of some whisky which he had drunk." The quantity consumed is not recorded. The boy's mother did not seek medical advice until some 15 hours later. This was, it is reported, "too late for he died soon afterwards."

If you don't want whiskey to get the better of you, drink the best of whiskey.
                    -Father Mathew (an Irish priest of the early 19th century).

FEBRUARY

1

1896-Mr. A. Edwards announces his intention to build "a commodious distillery" on the Aultmore property.

2 *Inter House Skiing*

Candlemas

3

1900-Messrs. Alex Fraser & Co. of Glenburgie distillery presented 20 cases of his whisky to Lord Lovat's Scouts who were serving in South Africa during the Boer War. The whisky was specially bottled and appropriately labelled.

Senior Science Talk

4

1897-Banffshire Advertiser announced that the West Brewery in Elgin was to be converted into a distillery which was to be called Glen Moray.

5

1901-Glen Elgin "exposed for sale at auction", but withdrawn when it did not reach the upset price of £5,000.

6 *Leave*

1605-Glasgow's incorporation of Maltmen was incorporated by Letter of Guildry.

7 *Leave*

1901-Glenburgie distillery bought at auction by Mr. J.A. Johnston.

WHISKY IN SHERRY CASKS

Until 1983, almost all sherry sold in the United Kingdom was shipped in casks and bottled in Britain. These empty casks were then surplus to the sherry shippers' requirements. Likewise, the unions in the United States had great power at the beginning of the 20th century and forced the United States government to write into U.S. law that a bourbon cask could only be used once, thus protecting the jobs of U.S. coopers. The Scots, being very economical, were able to buy these second-hand casks very cheaply. This Scots canniness brought about a fortunate accident - that Scotch Whisky matures well in either sherry or bourbon casks. Since 1983, however, all sherry must be bottled in Jerez. To maintain continuity of supply of good quality sherry casks, some distillers have casks made up by cooperages in Spain and lend them to sherry bodegas for three to four years. The Scotch Whisky producers then dictate what style of sherry should be aged (or fermented) in the casks. They then have more control over the final Scottish product. The down side is that a sherry butt now costs in the region of £350.00!

AGED FOR A MINIMUM THREE YEARS

Lloyd George, that great anti-alcohol reforming prime minister, did the whisky industry a great service by forcing through the Immature Spirits (Restriction) Act in 1925. This laid down that, in order to be called "Scotch Whisky", the spirit must be aged for a minimum of three years in oak casks. Until this date, only the wealthy could afford the luxury of ageing their whisky for any more than an absolute minimum. Most bottled whiskies had been aged for some time, but the time period has now been "set out in stone" in European Community legislation.

THE COOPER

Although a cooperage does not have the work and therefore the importance which it once held, a cooper remains a craftsman - he takes straight planks of wood and shapes them into an almost spherical hollow shape which is watertight. He does all this without the aid of glue or nails. His tools remain as they always have: the adze, the hammer and the saw.

SIZES OF CASKS AND RESPECTIVE CAPACITIES:

Cask	Approximate content in litres
Butt	500
Hogshead	250-305
American Barrel	173-191
Quarter	127-159
Octave	45-68

Verily Scotland is well watered.
        -The (Irish) Whiskey Trade Review,
                February 17th, 1893.

8 1st Contract

1587-Mary, Queen of Scots was beheaded at
Fotheringay Castle.

9 Visit To Scottish Textiles College
Visit To Newi 1pm

10

1905-Dalwhinnie distillery sold to Cook &
Bernheimer of New York for £1,250.

11 Ski day

12

13

1692-Massacre of Glencoe.

14

WHISKY OR TEA

When Mortlach distillery was established, it used the water of **The Priests' Well** which "is a large and beautiful spring of excellent water - water in fact, that could not be surpassed either for making Whisky or for infusing that less powerful narcotic - tea."

GLENGOYNE DISTILLERY

GLEN GRANT BURN

The Glen Grant burn runs down the hill past Glen Grant distillery. In the latter part of the 19th century, James Grant the younger, known as "the Major" built a dram safe into the rocks by this burn. Guests at dinner were encouraged to take a post-prandial stroll through the grounds of the major's home. Their path would invariably take them through the gardens to where the burn flows through a small gorge and where the dram safe is situated. Here the Major would stop and remove from the safe, which is well disguised, a bottle of Glen Grant and glasses. His enthralled audience would enjoy their dram diluted with the vigorous waters of the Glen Grant burn. The dram safe remains to this day and is used by the distillery manager to entertain his guests.

ADDITIONS TO WHISKY

Scotch Whisky is a drink to be enjoyed. The international opinion seems to be that the finer Scotches must be drunk neat, or if anything is to be added, then only more whisky should be added.

The addition of water releases the esters and aldehydes, compounds which contribute to the aroma, and makes the contents of your glass a bigger drink in more than just volume, but it also means that it is longer until you have to approach the bar for another drink. A truly Scottish outlook on the problem!

Drinking neat whisky can also cause indigestion. The addition of water at one third water to two-thirds whisky (at 40% vol.) is very much a personal choice - even with the finest single malts. Whatever you wish to add to your whisky is fine as it is an infinitely mixable and adaptable drink.

In Germany a popular drink is whisky and orange juice, in the Caribbean, it is whisky and milk, in the "pubs" of Glasgow whisky and lemonade is popular and a director of one of the old D.C.L. companies horrified his fellow directors by insisting on drinking his whisky with Cola!

GLEN GRANT DISTILLERY

But you've no idea what a difference it makes,
mixing it with other things.
-Scotch, Sir Robert Bruce Lockhart

FEBRUARY

15

1980-Macallan distillery installs waste heat
recovery system.

16

1983-Scottish Malt Distilleries announce closure
of 11 distilleries.

17

18 ½ term

19 ½ term

1894-Convalmore distillery begins working.

20 ½ term

21 ½ term

1895-The roof of a duty free warehouse at Glen
Rothes distillery collapsed under "the great
weight of snow".

CAMPBELTOWN

Campbeltown was once a thriving whisky region. The town had plentiful supplies of good water, had a fully operational coalfield on its doorstep and is in a fairly arable region of the country. By 1920 there were 20 distilleries operational in the district.

- Albyn
- Argyll
- Campbeltown
- Dalintober
- Glengyle
- Glen Scotia
- Hazelburn
- Kintyre
- Lochruan
- Springbank
- Ardlussa
- Benmore
- Dalaruan
- Drumore
- Glen Nevis
- Glenside
- Kinloch
- Lochhead
- Rieclachan
- Springside

Of these, now only **Glen Scotia** and **Springbank** are operational, although there is another single malt produced within the building of Springbank - **Longrow**. The building contains three stills: one wash and two spirit. They both share the same wash still, but the first spirit still produces "Springbank" and the second, "Longrow".

REWARD FOR REPORTING THE "WORM"

During the 18th century, a reward of £5 was offered to anyone reporting the location of an illicit still. The most expensive part of the illicit distiller's equipment was the *worm*, a coil of copper pipe through which the evaporated spirit passes, condensing into liquid form and running off as spirit, or Uisgebaugh. When the worm was worn out, the distiller would dismantle the still, cannily saving anything which might be of use in the future, but ensuring that enough was left to show that a still had been in use. The distiller would then contact the gauger (exciseman) and tell him that he had discovered a still. He would receive the £5 reward, with which he would buy more copper to make a new worm and set the new still up at another site.

LOCHRUAN DISTILLERY

Campbeltown Loch I wish you were Whisky,
Campbeltown Loch, Och Aye!
Campbeltown Loch I wish you were Whisky,
I would drink you dry.

-Old Scottish song.

22 ½ term ends

23

24 Visit to Scottish Textiles College 1pm

25 Skiiday

1965-Moffat distillery produced its first spirit.

26

27

1919-Electric light installed at Cragganmore distillery.

28

1898-Benromach Distillery Company advertises for contractors to build the distillery.

A TIMELESS CHARACTER

Centuries ago a waterfall in a secluded glen on the southern slopes of the Highlands provided a safe location for the secret distilling of Highland Malt Whisky.

Almost 160 years ago the government of the day licensed Glengoyne Distillery, where today, some 30,000 visitors a year see the distillers at work. They learn how the simple ingredients of water, unpeated malted barley and yeast are magically transformed into the spirit which long years of maturation allow to become Glengoyne Single Highland Malt Scotch Whisky.

Visitors to the Distillery have an opportunity to tour "number 2 warehouse", which has now been converted to show the history of Scotch Whisky distillation at Glengoyne over the years.

A "wee dram" of Glengoyne - which allows visitors to see how the use of unpeated barley lets all the distinctive flavours of Glengoyne show through, is followed by a tour to see the Distillery at work.

Special facilities have recently been installed to allow the disabled to enjoy a visit to Glengoyne. Tutored Nosing Sessions are held every Wednesday evening which allow the inquisitive to study Glengoyne and other malt whiskies in-depth and through "Nosing" to understand how time and different varieties of cask can affect the end product.

Glengoyne is situated 15 miles north of Glasgow on the A81 in the lovely historic Blanc Valley and close to Loch Lomond and the village of Killearn.